More about myself

Today's date _____.

My full name is _____.

My address is _____

_____.

Answer these questions with **sentences**.

1 Have you ever lived anywhere else? _____

_____.

2 Where have you been on holiday? _____

_____.

3 At what time do you usually get up in the morning?

_____.

4 At what time do you usually go to bed at night?

_____.

5 At what time does morning school start?

_____.

6 At what time does afternoon school end?

_____.

7 What do you do at the week-end? _____

_____.

Give a description of yourself. It must be clear enough for anyone coming
into the room to recognise you straight away.

Here are some words you may need.

blond	**colour**	**hair**	**slim**	**thin**
build	**dark**	**height**	**spectacles**	**wearing**
clothes	**eyes**	**short**	**tall**	**well-built**

_____

_____

_____

_____

_____

Where are they ?

A group of children are enjoying themselves in an adventure playground.

above	beneath	in front of	left	over	under
along	between	inside	on top of	right	up
behind	down	into	out of	through	

From this list, write the correct words in each sentence to describe where the children are. You must use each one once only.

1 Mark is climbing _____ the tree.

2 David is peeping _____ the wall.

3 Sophie is sliding _____ the chute.

4 Karen is sitting _____ the chute.

5 Paul is crawling _____ the pipe.

6 Ann is hiding _____ the shelter.

7 Alison is standing _____ the box.

8 Jim is standing _____ the shelter and the box.

9 Lauren is pouring water _____ a bucket _____ the bath.

10 Thomas is _____ the wall. He has a sword in his _____ hand and a shield on his _____ arm.

11 Alan is kneeling _____ Thomas.

12 Clare is creeping _____ the wall.

13 Alan is _____ Jim.

14 David is _____ the wall.

Page 2

Last to first

The **last letter** of one word is the same as the **first letter** of the next word.
Putting one letter in each square, write the word for each of these pictures.

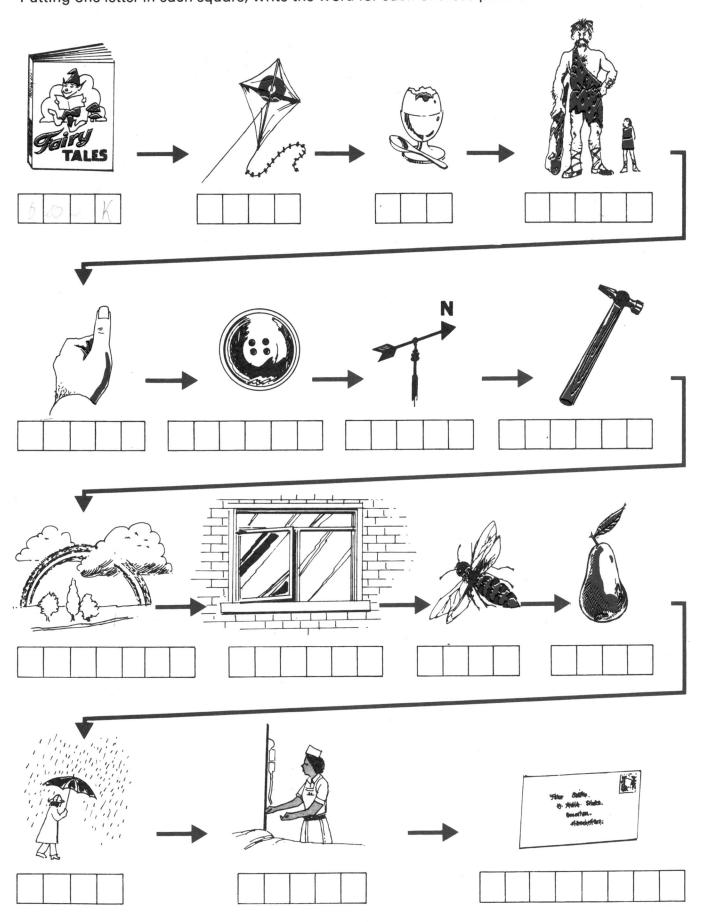

What are they doing ?

Complete these sentences by writing a word in the space to say what each one is doing.
The sentences have the same numbers as the pictures.

1 Paul is _____ on the fence.

2 Sue is _____ up the leaves.

3 Mrs. Morris is _____ her car.

4 Mr. Morris is _____ a button on his coat.

5 Kim is _____ some jam tarts.

6 David is _____ his jersey on the line.

7 Laura is _____ the mirror.

8 Grandma is _____ the pram.

9 Keith is _____ a trolley of logs.

10 The cat is _____ a bird.

11 The clown is _____ off the step-ladder.

12 Mr. Sykes is _____ his front door.

Verbs

A verb is a "doing word".

All the words you have filled in on page 4 are **verbs**.

They describe the **actions** taking place in each picture.

These are the **verbs** you could have used. They are printed in pairs.

chasing , scaring	;	cleaning , washing	;	making , baking
falling , tumbling	;	hanging , pegging	;	painting , decorating
polishing , wiping	;	pulling , hauling	;	pushing , wheeling
sewing , stitching	;	sitting , resting	;	sweeping , clearing

From each pair in this list, there is at least one **verb** you did not use on page 4.

Use it now in the same sentence.

1 Paul is _____ on the fence.

2 Sue is _____ up the leaves.

3 Mrs. Morris is _____ her car.

4 Mr. Morris is _____ a button on his coat.

5 Kim is _____ some jam tarts.

6 David is _____ his jersey on the line.

7 Laura is _____ the mirror.

8 Grandma is _____ the pram.

9 Keith is _____ a trolley of logs.

10 The cat is _____ a bird.

11 The clown is _____ off the step-ladder.

12 Mr. Sykes is _____ his front door.

Find ten **verbs** in this list of words and write them below.

day	night	crawled	ran	book	sat	walked
boy	men	started	stopped	early	some	fell
August	jumped	one	skipped	time	hopped	

The ten **verbs**, which describe actions, are _____

_____

_____ .

Verbs

A verb is a "doing word". It describes an action.
Underline all the **verbs** in these poems. The first two are done for you.

The House that Jack built

This is the cock that crowed in the morn

That waked the priest all shaven and shorn

That married the man all tattered and torn

That kissed the maiden all forlorn

That milked the cow with the crumpled horn

That tossed the dog

That worried the cat

That killed the rat

That ate the malt that lay in the house that Jack built.

Mr. East

Mr. East gave a feast,

Mr. North laid the cloth,

Mr. West took the best,

Mr. South burned his mouth,—

He ate some hot potato!

Hey Diddle Diddle

Hey diddle diddle, the cat and the fiddle,

The cow jumped over the moon;

The little dog laughed to see such sport,

And the dish ran away with the spoon.

The Giant

Fee, fie, fo, fum!

I smell the blood of an Englishman.

Be he alive, or be he dead,

I'll grind his bones to make my bread.

Verbs

A Write a **verb** in each space to describe what happens in the morning.

"I _____ up early each morning. I _____ my teeth and

_____ my hands and face. I _____ on my clothes.

I _____ my breakfast and _____ off to school.

I _____ to my friends before the bell _____.

School _____ with assembly, and then we _____ lessons."

B Write a **sentence** in answer to each of these questions.

Underline the **verbs** in each of your answers.

1 What do you do before you eat an orange?

_____.

2 How does a referee start a football match?

_____.

3 How do you lock a door?

_____.

4 How does a conductor control an orchestra?

_____.

5 How do you tell the time?

_____.

6 What happens if you cut your finger?

_____.

7 What do you do before posting a letter?

_____.

8 What does a kennel-maid do for a living?

_____.

9 What do you do on a friend's birthday?

_____.

10 What do you do with most of your pocket-money?

_____.

Crosswords

Name the animals

Follow the arrows. Write a letter in each square.

A page from the calendar

March						
Monday	**Tuesday**	**Wednesday**	**Thursday**	**Friday**	**Saturday**	**Sunday**
	1	2	3	4	5	6
7	8	9	10	11	12	13
14	15	16	17	18	19	20
21	22	23	24	25	26	27
28	29	30	31			

Imagine that today is **Thursday, 17th March**.

Complete these sentences.

1 **Tomorrow** will be _____, _____.
                               (day)   (date)

2 **Yesterday** was _____, _____.
                           (day)   (date)

3 The date **next Thursday** will be _____.

4 **A week ago** the date was _____.

5 **A fortnight today** will be _____, _____.
                               (day)   (date)

6 Before today _____ days of March had passed.

   After today we still have _____ more days in March.

7 Next month, which is _____, will begin on a _____

8 Last month, which was called _____, ended on a _____

9 The other months which, like March, have **thirty-one days**, are

   _____, _____, _____,

   _____, _____ and _____.

10 The Parent-Teacher Association always meets on the **second Tuesday** of each month.

    The **last** meeting was on _____, _____.
                                    (day)   (date)

    The **next** meeting will be on _____, _____.
                                      (day)   (date)

Placings

This is a plan showing where some children live.

Abbey Road	○ Kevin	○ Paul	⑥ Jane	Gibson's Garage	High Street

Franklin Road

Abbey Road	○ The Corner Shop	○ Sunita	○ Alan	③ Ann	① David	High Street

A Write the number of the house inside each empty circle.

> **at the corner of** **between** **next door to** **opposite**

B Using the number of the house and any of these words, write each child's answer to the question, **"Where do you live?"** The first one is done for you.

1 Alan *"I live at 5 Franklin Road, between Ann and Shirley and opposite Jane."*

2 Ann

3 David

4 Jane

5 Kevin

6 Paul

7 Sunita

C In the same way, write **your** answer to the question, **"Where do you live ?"**

Page 10

What are they doing—and why ?

Write a sentence to describe what each person is doing, and why he or she is doing it.
You will need these words.

drying	ploughing	dog	radiator	broken	parcel
filling	pumping	doorbell	tyre	empty	ready
measuring	ringing	field	window	flat	wet

1

1 Jill is _____ her _____

because _____

_____ .

2

2 Dad is _____

_____ .

3

3 Mum is _____

_____ .

4

4 Luke is _____

_____ .

5

5 The farmer is _____

_____ .

6

6 The postman is _____

_____ .

Words in a dictionary

A By putting a letter in each square, complete each word after its meaning.

B In column B, write the five words of each group in correct alphabetical order, as they would appear in a dictionary.

> **To find the correct alphabetical order, look at the fourth letter of each word.**

Words starting with bra

Meaning	A Word	B Alphabetical order
the arm-like limb of a tree	b r a _ _ _	1
a yellowish metal	b r a _	2
the part on a vehicle used for stopping or slowing down	b r a _ _	3
the mark made with a hot iron	b r a _ _	4
the bush on which blackberries grow	b r a _ _ _ _	5

Words starting with har

Meaning	A Word	B Alphabetical order
an animal like a large rabbit	h a r _	1
a shelter for boats	h a r _ _ _	2
a crop of food gathered in	h a r _ _ _	3
firm or difficult	h a r _	4
a spear used for killing whales	h a r _ _ _ _	5

Words starting with thi

Meaning	A Word	B Alphabetical order
a metal cap used on the finger when sewing	t h i _ _ _ _	1
a prickly plant with purple flowers	t h i _ _ _	2
a person who steals	t h i _ _	3
three tens	t h i _ _	4
the part of the leg between the body and the knee	t h i _ _	5

Reading a block graph

The class made a block graph entitled **"Type of home"**.

Each one had to put a dot by the type of home in which he or she lived. This was the result.

Type of home

Type of home																				
House	●	●	●	●	●	●	●	●	●	●	●	●	●	●	●	●	●	●		
Bungalow	●	●	●	●	●	●	●													
Flat	●	●	●	●	●	●	●	●	●											

0　　　　　5　　　　　10　　　　　15　　　　　20
Number of children

A Answer each question by writing a **sentence**.

1 In what type of home do **most** children in this class live?

_____.

2 In what type of home do the **least** number of children in this class live?

_____.

3 How many children altogether recorded a dot?

_____.

B The children could have drawn pictures instead of dots. Draw a suitable picture in each of these squares.

House   Bungalow   Flat

C These are types of **houses**.

a detached house

two semi-detached houses

a row of terraced houses

Write a sentence about each type of house.

1 A detached house _____.

2 A semi-detached house _____.

3 A terraced house _____.

D Why does the council build **bungalows** for old people?

_____.

Group words

Write each of these words in its correct group.

ant	buttercup	daisy	moth	robin	thrush
ash	butterfly	earwig	oak	rose	wasp
bee	chestnut	elm	ostrich	snowdrop	wren
beech	daffodil	magpie	pansy	sparrow	yew

Birds

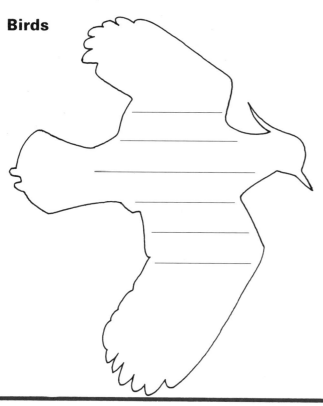

Flowers

Insects

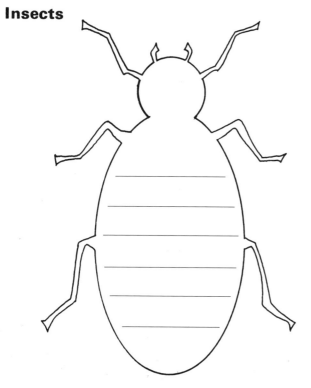

Trees

How do they feel ?

A Here are five **adjectives** which tell how a person feels.

> angry   happy   nervous   sad   worried

Write the most suitable of these five adjectives in each of these sentences.

1 Before trying her first dive, Clare felt very _____ .

2 Amil was _____ when he found that Floppy, his rabbit, had died.

3 Mrs. Miller shook her fist at the boys. She looked very _____ .

4 Jane was over an hour late from school, and her mother was very _____ .

5 The kitten has settled down and is quite _____ in its new home.

B Here are five adjectives with similar meanings to those in Section A.

> annoyed   contented   frightened   sorrowful   upset

Copy out the sentences from Section A, but use these adjectives instead of the first five.

1 Before _____ .

2 Amil was _____ .

3 Mrs. Miller _____ .

4 Jane _____ .

5 The kitten _____ .

C

> astonished   cool   ill   surprised
> awkward   drowsy   merry   tearful
> cheery   famished   mournful   unruffled
> clumsy   hungry   sleepy   unwell

From this list, choose two adjectives which have the same meaning as the adjective in each of these sentences. Write them after the sentence.

1 Derek had a late night and felt very **tired**. _____ _____

2 He had not eaten and was **starving**. _____ _____

3 Emma was **amazed** at the number of gifts. _____ _____

4 The lost child was **miserable**. _____ _____

5 Sally is absent because she is **sick**. _____ _____

6 In an emergency a nurse must be **calm**. _____ _____

7 When he first tried skating, Duncan felt **unsteady**. _____ _____

8 Grandpa is such a **jolly** person. _____ _____

Page 15

Similar—but different

These sentences are about things which are **similar** in some ways, but **different** in others.

Write the correct word in each space.

1 Both are **utensils in the kitchen**.

A _____ has a handle and a spout. Water is boiled in it.

A _____ has a handle and a spout. Boiling water is poured into it to make tea.

2 Both are **joints in your body**.

Your _____ is between your arm and your hand.

Your _____ is between your leg and your foot.

3 Both are **winter months**. _____ is the first month of the year,

but _____ is the last month of the year.

4 Both are **drinks**. _____ is made from grapes, but

_____ is made from apples.

5 Both are **children in the same family**.

A _____ is a boy, but a _____ is a girl.

6 Both are **colours**. _____ is made from white and black,

but _____ is made from white and red.

7 Both are **areas of grass**.

A _____ is kept cut and tidy, but animals are allowed to graze in

a _____ .

8 Both are **kinds of meat**. _____ comes from a pig, but

_____ comes from a sheep.

9 Both appear on **television**. A _____ tells jokes, but a

_____ reads the news.

10 Both are **precious metals**. _____ is yellow in colour, but

_____ is white.

A story in pictures

A This is the story of **Larry's Lucky Find**.

These sentences tell the story, but they are in the wrong order.

> Soon, Larry was sure he felt a strong tug on his line.
> At the police station they were delighted with Larry.
> Larry decided, one day, to go fishing in the river.
> To his surprise, he saw that he had hooked a silver cup.
> He baited his hook, and cast his line into the water.

Write the sentences in the correct order.

1 _____

2 _____

3 _____

4 _____

5 _____

B This is the story, in pictures, of **Ann's Visit to the Park.**

Write the story in words, basing each sentence on a picture.

1 _____

2 _____

3 _____

4 _____

5 _____

About a car

(A) From this list, write the correct name in each label.

> body   bumper   headlights   number-plate   roof   window   windscreen
>
> bonnet   door   mirrors   radiator grille   wheels   windscreen-wipers

1 _____

2 _____

3 _____

4 _____

5 _____

6 _____

7 _____

8 _____

9 _____

10 _____

11 _____

12 _____

13 _____

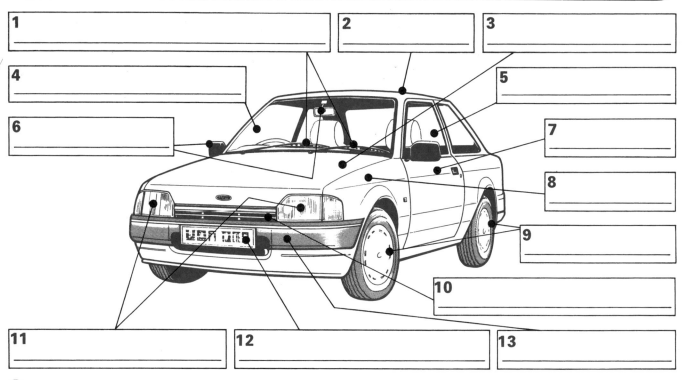

(B) After each of these clues, write the name of the part of a car from the above list.

a If you want to see the engine, lift this up. _____

b This keeps off the wind and rain,
and may shatter if hit by a stone. _____

c This is in front of a water-tank. _____

d Through these you can see anyone following or overtaking. _____

e One at the back and one at the front are ready
to take the first shock of a collision. _____

f Most cars have a spare one, in case of a puncture. _____

g Useful at night, these must not dazzle other drivers. _____

h These keep your view clear in rain, mud or mist. _____

i Open this if you want fresh air on your journey. _____

j This carries your registration letters and number. _____

(C) 1 Find the registration number of a car
and write it in this space.

2 At which place was the car first licensed? _____

3 In what year was it first licensed? _____

Singular words and plural words

A Some singular words having the letter **f** can be made into plural words by changing the letter **f** into a letter **v**. The plural word must end in **es**.

For example, **calf** (singular) becomes **calves** (plural).

In this table, write in the missing singular or plural word.

Singular	Plural	Singular	Plural
elf	_____	self	_____
half	_____	_____	sheaves
knife	_____	shelf	_____
_____	leaves	_____	thieves
life	_____	_____	wives
_____	loaves	wolf	_____

B Find the **plural word** for each of these.

one deer—forty _____ ;   one foot—two _____ ;

one mouse—three _____ ;   one sheep—fifty _____ ;

one tooth—twenty _____ .

C Find the **singular word** for each of these.

 This is a bag of **potatoes**. ➤ This _____ is not cooked properly.

 This is a tray of **tomatoes**. ➤ One _____ is enough for me, thank you.

This cave is full of **echoes**. ➤ I can only hear

one _____ .

 There are no **volcanoes** in this country. ➤ Mount Etna is a

famous _____ in Sicily.

Welcome to the World-wide Show!

This is how the ring-master introduces himself to the audience, before he brings on all the other artistes.

I am **R**onald the **r**enowned **r**ingmaster from **R**angoon!

(He makes it sound important by repeating the letter **r**.)

Using names and words from these lists, make up important-sounding introductions for each of these artistes.

Alice	clever	cowgirl	Denmark
Clara	happy	giant	Japan
Colin	tricky	juggler	Scotland
Dora	athletic	trapezist	Trinidad
Gerry	jolly	acrobat	Holland
Harry	dazzling	dog-trainer	Cuba
Jim	comical	clown	Australia
Steven	smiling	horseman	Canada
Tracey	gigantic	stilt-walker	Germany

1 Here is _____

the _____

_____

from _____ .

6 Presenting _____

the _____

_____

from _____ .

2 Welcome to _____

the _____

_____

from _____ .

7 The one and only _____

the _____

_____

from _____ .

3 This is _____

the _____

_____

from _____ .

8 And now, _____

the _____

_____

from _____ .

4 We now have _____

the _____

_____

from _____ .

9 Give a cheer for _____

the _____

_____

from _____ .

5 A big hand, please for

_____

the _____

from _____ .

10

In the last space, make up a drawing and an introduction of yourself.

Using a comma

> A **comma** is used when we make a list in a sentence but not usually before **and** or **or**.
> For example: Linda, Paul, Stephen, Kim and David all live in the same street.

A Put **commas** in these sentences.

1 Beef   mutton   lamb   veal and pork are all kinds of meat.

2 England   Scotland   Wales and Northern Ireland are countries of the United Kingdom.

3 At the zoo we saw lions   tigers   monkeys   giraffes   penguins and an elephant.

4 You can eat an egg raw   boiled   scrambled   fried   poached or in an omelette.

5 The colours of the rainbow are red   orange   yellow   green   blue   indigo and violet.

B Complete these sentences by making a list of **at least four things or people**.
Put **commas** in the correct places.

1 If I am going to paint a picture I need _____

_____ .

2 The different flavours you can buy from your ice-cream man are _____

_____ .

3 If the boys in this class had to empty their pockets, you would find they had

_____

_____ in them.

4 If I have a birthday party I will invite _____

_____ .

5 In a tool-shed I would expect to find _____

_____ .

6 A greengrocer sells _____

_____ .

7 The names of some of the streets or roads where children in this school live are

_____

_____ .

8 To print my name with a rubber stamp I need the letters _____

_____ .

Last two to first two

The **last two letters** of the first word are the **first two letters** of the second word.

For example,

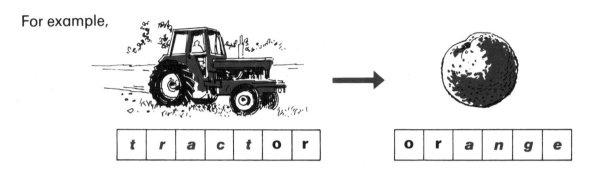

t	r	a	c	t	o	r

o	r	a	n	g	e

Follow the same rule to find each of these words, putting one letter in each square.

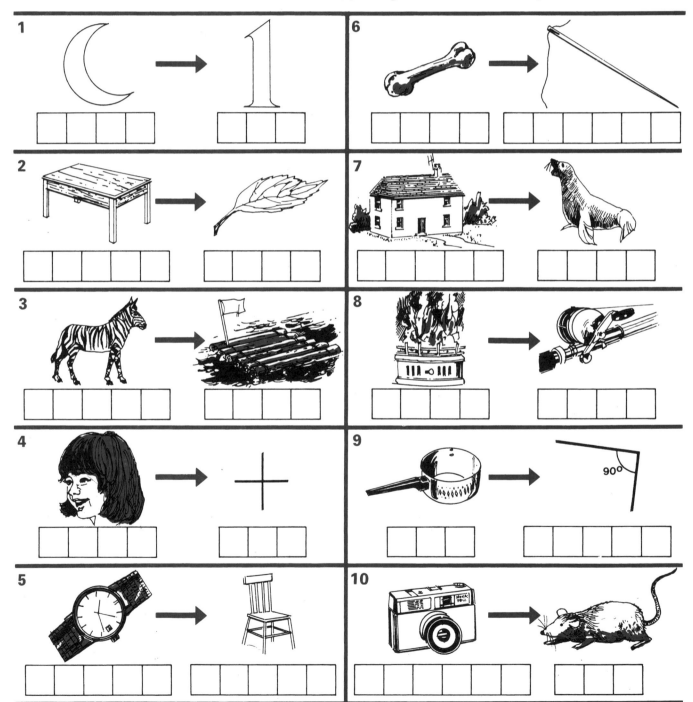

Follow the instructions carefully.

1 Put a dot in **every** square.

2 Put a dot in **alternate** squares.

3 Put a dot in every square **except** the first two and the last two.

4 Put a dot in the **first**, **middle** and **last** squares.

5 Put a dot in **all but** the middle square.

6 Draw a **diagonal** line, from corner to corner, in every square. Do this in the **same** direction in every square.

7 Draw a diagonal line, from corner to corner, in every square so that each square is **different** from its neighbour.

8 Write a letter in each square to spell a word on this page.

9 Putting one letter in each square, write the first seven letters of the alphabet in their **correct order**.

10 Putting one letter in each square, write the last seven letters of the alphabet in their **reverse order**.

11 Putting one letter in each square, write the **first letter** of the name of each day of the week in correct order.

12 Putting one letter in each square, write the seven **capital** letters of the alphabet which look just the same **upside down**.

A B C D E F G H I J K L M N O P Q R S T U V W X Y Z

Collective nouns

A **collective noun** is the name of a group or **collection** of things or people.

For example, a **range** of mountains ; a **squad** of footballers.

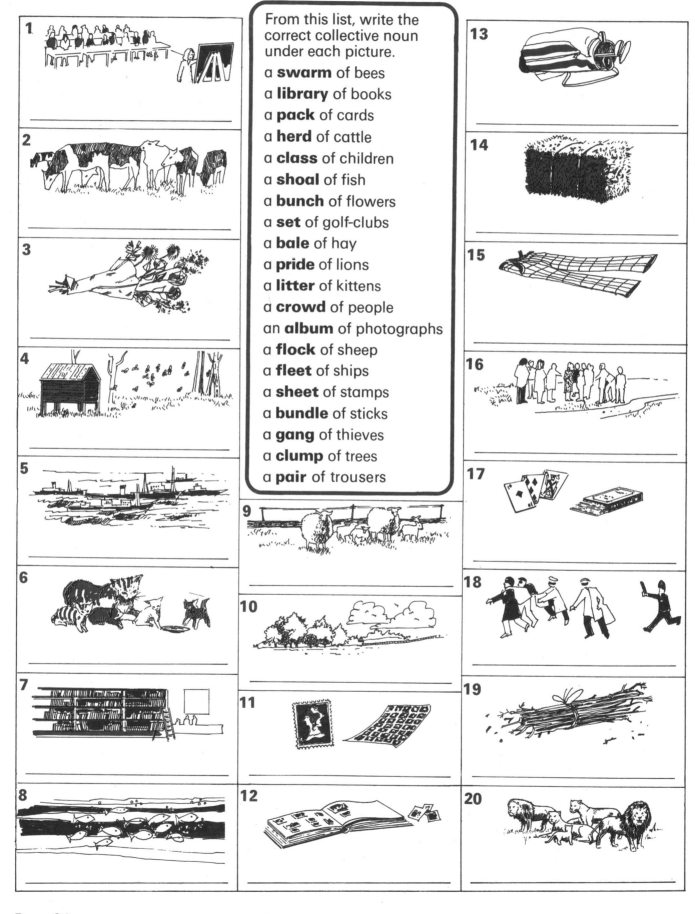

From this list, write the correct collective noun under each picture.

- a **swarm** of bees
- a **library** of books
- a **pack** of cards
- a **herd** of cattle
- a **class** of children
- a **shoal** of fish
- a **bunch** of flowers
- a **set** of golf-clubs
- a **bale** of hay
- a **pride** of lions
- a **litter** of kittens
- a **crowd** of people
- an **album** of photographs
- a **flock** of sheep
- a **fleet** of ships
- a **sheet** of stamps
- a **bundle** of sticks
- a **gang** of thieves
- a **clump** of trees
- a **pair** of trousers

Collective nouns

From the list of **collective nouns** in the panel on page 24, write the correct words in each of these sentences.

1 Each teacher looks after _____.

2 The fox is chased by _____.

3 Grandad likes to show us _____ taken when he was a boy.

4 The bank had been raided by _____.

5 The angler was excited to see _____.

6 You may be stung if you disturb _____.

7 Our cat has just had _____.

8 We know of several birds' nests in _____ over there.

9 In _____ there should be four suits of thirteen each.

10 A caddy carries _____ round the course.

11 The shepherd was bringing _____ down the hillside.

12 Collectors sometimes buy _____ when there is a new issue.

13 At our school we have _____ in each class-room.

14 When the pop star stepped off the train he was soon surrounded by _____ asking for his autograph.

15 Coming out of the harbour was _____ led by a destroyer.

16 At the cub camp my job was to gather _____ for the fire.

17 The farmer was driving _____ to the milking shed.

18 For one of our presents, we gave Mum _____ from the garden.

19 In winter, a pony will need _____ every week.

20 We all laughed when Tom put on _____ belonging to his older brother.

Start with S

The teacher said to the class, "Draw a letter **S** on your paper. Draw a picture so that the shape of the letter **S** is part of the picture — but the name of what you draw must begin with **S**."

Here are the best pictures. Write the correct name under each one.

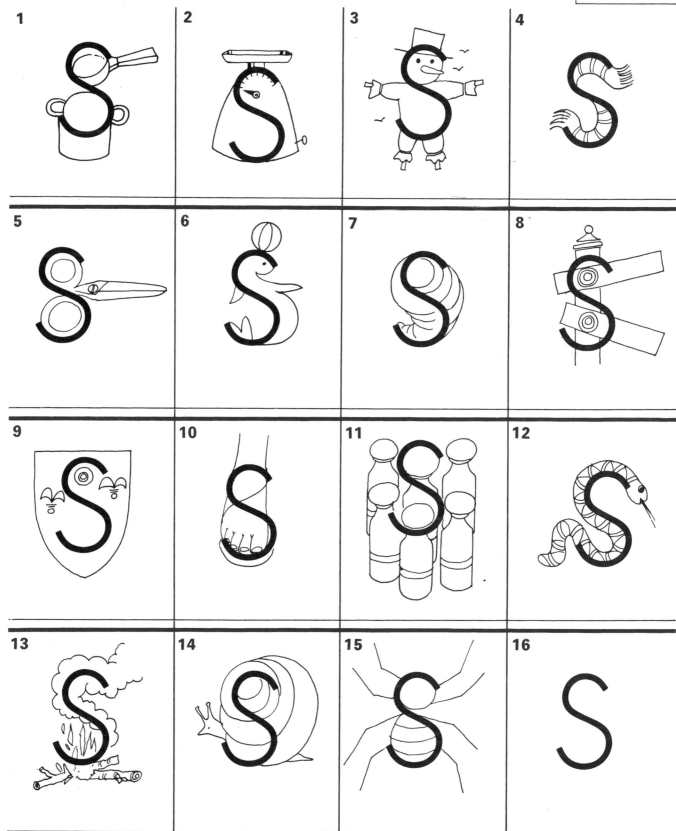

The last space is for your picture. Make the **S** into a large white water-bird.

Double vowels

The five **vowels** are **a e i o u** .

Many words have two vowels together.

Here are some words with **double vowels**.

b**ea**r   p**ai**r   fl**oo**r   r**ee**d   m**ou**se   g**ui**ld

ai	au	ea	ee	ei	eo	ie	io	oa	oe	oi	oo	ou	ue	ui

A From this list of double vowels write the correct ones to complete the words in these sentences.

1 L_____k before you l_____p.

2 T_____ many c_____ks sp_____l the broth.

3 A p_____r of sh_____s sh_____ld match _____ch other.

4 Fresh fr_____t is g_____d for y_____r h_____lth.

5 Put y_____r dog on its l_____d and so av_____d any tr_____ble with other

   p_____ple on the r_____d.

6 _____gust is the _____ghth month of the y_____r.

7 Co_____ is a drink made from s_____ds called b_____ns.

8 Who t_____d this knot? That is the q_____stion.

9 There is a g_____d v_____w from the flat r_____f of this h_____se.

10 The t_____cher s_____d, "I want y_____ to s_____ how n_____t and

    tidy is P_____l's writing in his English work b_____k."

B Complete these notices with **double vowels**.

1  L_____k _____t!
   There's a th_____f ab_____t.

2 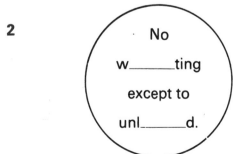 No
   w_____ting
   except to
   unl_____d.

3 Pl_____se form a q_____
   _____tside the stat_____n.

4 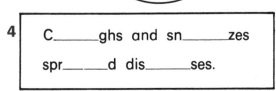 C_____ghs and sn_____zes
   spr_____d dis_____ses.

Somewhere in the house

You may have some, or all, of these things somewhere in your house.

trunk	treacle	tack	tap	towel
tank	torch	tomato	toast	tie
telephone	tablespoon	thread	toy	taper
tape	tea	television	tray	thermometer
ticket	trap			

A From the above list, write the correct word before its meaning.

1 _____ — a large serving-spoon

2 _____ — a short broad-headed nail

3 _____ — a large water-container

4 _____ — a short outlet pipe which can be opened or stopped

5 _____ — a long ribbon of cloth

6 _____ — a long narrow candle

7 _____ — dried leaves of a plant from which a drink is brewed

8 _____ — apparatus by which one person can speak to another at a distance

9 _____ — apparatus for receiving pictures sent by radio

10 _____ — an instrument for measuring temperature

11 _____ — strong cotton used in sewing

12 _____ — small card used as a pass or receipt

13 _____ — a narrow piece of cloth worn round the neck

14 _____ — a slice of bread which has been scorched on both sides

15 _____ — a red fruit used in salads

16 _____ — an electric hand-lamp

17 _____ — a cloth for wiping or drying

18 _____ — a plaything

19 _____ — a piece of apparatus used for catching mice

20 _____ — a flat piece of wood or metal for carrying things

21 _____ — a thick, sweet syrup obtained from sugar

22 _____ — a large chest or packing-case

B Put a tick ✓ in front of the number of any of these that you have in your house **but** only if you can tell your friend exactly where it is.